C000225305

The FISHING Cartoon Book

Edited by Robert Welsh

David & Charles
Newton Abbot London North Pomfret (Vt) Vancouver

ISBN 0 7153 7396 X

Library of Congress Catalog Card Number 77-076099

Set in 12 on 13pt Bembo
and printed in Great Britain
by Redwood Burn Limited
for David & Charles (Publishers) Limited
Brunel House Newton Abbot Devon

Published in the United States of America
by David & Charles Inc
North Pomfret Vermont 05053 USA

Published in Canada
by Douglas David & Charles Limited
1875 Welch Street North Vancouver BC

CONTENTS

INTRODUCTION

One of the earliest words in the English language on fishing as a pastime was *The Treatyse of Fysshynge wyth an Angle* generally attributed to one Dame Juliana Barnes – an odd start to say the least – and printed at Westminster in 1496, although probably written some fifty years earlier.

The Treatyse captured, nearly five hundred years ago, the spirit of fishing with an angle in a few words that may be difficult to decipher but that will reward a moment's careful scanning:

> '. . . so I aske this question, wyche bynne the menys and cause to reduce a man to a mery spryte. (The angler) schall have hys holsom walke and mery at hys owne ease, and also many a sweyt eayr of divers erbis and flowres that schall make hym ryght hongre and well disposed in hys body. He schall heyr the melodies melodious of the ermony of byrde: he schall se also the yong swannes and signetes folowing ther eyrours, duckes, cootes, herons, and many other fowlys with ther brodys, wyche me semyt better then all the noyse of houndes, and blastes of hornes and other gamys that fawkners or hunters can make, and yf the angler take the fyssche, hardly then ys ther no man meryer then he in his sprites.'

The father of angling, Izaak Walton, used *The Treatyse* freely in his own immortal work *The Compleat Angler* as he used several other works – updated a couple of hundred years in literary style – and was even charged with plagiarism by some. But although his book may have been the child of a few, it has been the father of many. And Walton's work surpasses them all in charm and delight.

Izaak Walton (one is almost tempted to call him The Bard) wrote thus: 'The first is the dun fly in March: the body is made of dun wool, the wings of partridge feathers. The second is another dun fly: the body of black wool . . . ' while *The Treatyse* states: '*Marche*. The donne fly, the body of the donne woll, the wyngis of the pertryche. Another donne flye, the body of blacke woll . . . ' and so on almost word for word on occasion, and particularly when he lists his 'jury of twelve flies'.

However this is no treatise on Walton or on flies, and we have to move on nearly 200 years to note published humorous drawings of the subject, etchings that have a glimmer of understanding that the gentle art of fishing can be a subject for gentle mirth; in fact we move on to the early Victorians, whose humour was often of the most serious, reflecting consciously and unconsciously the defensive attitude of master to man, mistress to maid, as slowly and painfully the 'lower orders' pulled themselves up the ladder of acceptance.

However, fishing humour did not become a butt of socially discriminating humorists, as did horse-riding, dining-out, walking in the Park (there *was* only one Park) and was rarely derided as a lowly pastime, although until the 1880s it had little to commend it to Society, and was in fact the occupation of the ordinary cove.

Through the satirical magazines and such 'serio-comic' journals as London's *Judy*, as one of the main rivals of *Punch* called itself (it even used a similar cover illustration), Victorian humour steam-rollered its way into the world of laughter by deriding the lame, the backward, the poor, the servant, the bootblack – the minion and the menials – and (to be fair) the young bucks, whose foppish 'Don't yer know' comments were almost invariably lampooned. But it seemed to have left anglers to the mercies

CAUTION!

"I was gane to axe ye, Donald, if ye'd lend me a Half-Croon."
"Eh, Mon; I've got but one lendin' Half-Croon, an' that's oot just at present."

Judy, *once a sturdy rival of* Punch, *aimed socially downstream a little and captured a good readership.*

of their catch, without becoming unduly concerned with the catcher's station or his antecedents.

Other magazines that rivalled the doyen of them all, *Punch*, cast their nets in more socially downstream waters, hoping to reach the skilled artisan and modest professional readership. Doomed to eventual failure, *Fun* (1861–1901) was another blatant copy of *Punch* in format and general style aimed at this lower market – and held out for thirty years in the cut-throat game of winning readers. Even the illustrious W. S. Gilbert worked on it for a time on a freelance basis. When Gilbert offered a story and some poems to Mark Lemmon, the editor of *Punch* turned down the story as too red-blooded for his magazine – and would accept work from Gilbert only if he severed his relationships with *Fun*; an indication of the softening of the once-firebrand *Punch*, which was drifting towards establishment status, and the rise of rival and less political *Fun*, which lost out only by the uncertain quality of its humour.

Another brief butterfly of publishing, *Man in the Moon* (it lasted a full twenty-eight issues) concerned itself more with hostility to *Punch* than its own humorous content. Its main contributor Shirley Brookes, once turned down by *Punch*, later disciplined his flamboyant essays and succeeded Mark Lemmon in the editorial chair of *Punch*. Lesser so-called comic journals were *The Puppet Show* and *Pasquin*, both of which tried to needle *Punch* into indiscretions and both of which foundered on the sharp rocks of such manoeuvres. Another engendered by the *Punch* success, *The Tomahawk*, appeared in the 1860s, a more serious paper which carried straight news as well as humour. Its tinted cartoons were some claim to fame and its editor, Arthur a Beckett, finally made what seemed to be the obligatory move – he went to *Punch*. *Moonshine* was a later product first published in the 1880s with humour like a wet laundry bag. In the twentieth century only the *New Yorker* has risen to a status similar to Britain's premier humorous-satirical journal,

ATTACHED TO THE LINE.

but even with its attractive blend of short stories, impeccable features and sometimes freakish humour, it is often too 'intimate-review' to be appreciated away from the eastern seaboard of America.

The angler made his first appearance in the comic paper around the 1840s when small woodcuts depicting fish and fisher were used at column width to head-up features on everything but angling. The analogies and metaphors conjured up by rod, line, angler, bait and fishy victim could be used like the language of cricket and Alice in Wonderland to mean so much or so little in almost every walk of life. Thus the first small cut in *Punch* in issue No 6 underlines the difference in status – and treatment by authority – of gentlemen writing for the weekly journals and lowly penny-a-line journalists whose income was directly linked to the length of the column their words would occupy, by breaking the feature with an illustration of a fish talking to an angler, using a tag about being 'attached to the line'.

Other illuminated piscatorial puns – and this was an age of puns – could hinge upon things financial – 'an unexpected rise'; people with pleasant dispositions – 'merry old soles'; political text could be supported by 'a floating voter'. Great play was also made with bait, hook, cast, deep waters, and of course, piscator himself. The pun is, to modern ears, a groan joke and it is surprising that it lasted so long as a fashion in amusement. As one wit said, it is listened to for the speed at which it arrives and loved for the speed at which it is forgotten.

Iconoclastic satire tussled with jingoism in the crowded pages or almost all humorous journals – the Russian bear, the French prince, Mama and Papa and their little royal offspring (curiously, Queen V. was said to have enjoyed jokes about seasickness and, dare it be whispered, lavatorial subjects). These too were the days when every cartoon looked like a drawing by Phiz, Charles Dickens' faithful illustrator, and every young man looked like David Copperfield – line artist John Leech was superb at this type of innocence – and in the journals like *Judy*, *Fun* and *Punch*, the mood was often Dickensian, a sombre mood leavened with outbursts of ribald humour, acid attacks on foreign neighbours, pointed insults to politicians that were unfancied by the particular journal – and plenty of unbalanced pontifications about royalty. As a turn-of-the-century writer said

A TALE OF A WHALE.

F. M. THE DUKE OF WELLINGTON and the Margate Boatmen have been recently in the position of the Lion and the Unicorn, except that, instead of fighting for the crown, they have been fighting for a whale, which was fool enough to tumble like a great sand eel on to the sands of Margate. F. M. THE DUKE, treating as fish all that comes to his net, as Lord Warden of the Cinque Ports claimed his share of the prize, and refused to allow the captors to bone the whale for the sake of the whalebone. MR. WADDINGTON, the Margate surgeon, took up the matter on behalf of the boatmen, when F. M. THE DUKE OF WELLINGTON presents his "compliments" in a manner anything but complimentary. F. M. is not aware of any relationship between a Fellow of the Royal College of Surgeons and the Court of Admiralty of the Cinque Ports, and F. M. expresses his determination to dispose of the proceeds of his share of the whale without consulting the opinion of MR. WADDINGTON.

There is no doubt that F. M. is entitled to do as he pleases with his own; and if a donkey were to tumble over the cliffs, the Lord Warden might come into competition with other claimants for the carcase. We can imagine the DUKE's answering an application from a stranger something in the following manner:—"F. M. THE DUKE OF WELLINGTON presents his compliments to MR. BLANK. The DUKE is not aware that MR. BLANK has any relation with the Admiralty, or with the donkey found on the Margate Sands. F. M. THE DUKE will dispose of his own share of the proceeds of the donkey, and will be happy to hand over the skin to any one whom it may happen to fit, and who is entitled to wear it."

As Lord Warden of the Cinque Ports, F.M. (Field Marshal) the Duke of Wellington, retired from warlike occupations by the date of this drawing (1850) merits some criticism of his conduct here.

'These journals drew their material as freely from the most exalted spheres of foreign politics as from the provincial nursery, and dealing with every side of life are not less observant of the follies of Belgravia than of the peculiarities of Whitechapel'.

The tranquil waters of our gentle pastime however escaped this bustling scene, this turbulent inky war against our enemies, real or windmill fancy. Through the pages of popular journals sailed the light, leisurely, riverbank humour of the moment, a salve indeed after the controversial features of the day. From shivering before the upraised claw of the Russian bear or the later bayonet-points of the Kaiser's moustaches, the reader's eye would fall gratefully upon the fishing drawing, quiet, gently funny, with the type of fly in use or the contents of the gillie's hip flask as its most serious posers.

A century ago angling was not the high society sport it grew to be – part of the huntin' shootin' fishin' trilogy of rich men's games that it became later in the last century and the early part of this one. Then more the contemplative occupation of those who could afford only the time, fishing was the pastime of merchant or counterhand, old or young, idler or artisan. It cost nothing to fish after all, before the days of Scottish waters and gillies and expensive rod.

Neither were early cartoons the caricatures we now consider to be within the meaning of that word. Rather were they serious line works of the artist, carefully detailed in shape and texture (particularly when drawing room or country life scenes) and filled with pictorial information from corner to corner. Ladies all had faces like Rachel at the Well, great dark eyes, Grecian noses and classical monolithic bosoms – and were usually at least six feet tall. Only the lower orders could occasionally be caricatured, and their visages and poses were often portrayed as somewhat more than slightly simian . . .

The 'small cut' grew into the half page

engraving. This was still a woodcut made by sticking the drawing to a boxwood block (or the drawing itself sketched straight onto the face of the block with pen or pencil) the surface of which was then cut away by the wood engraver, leaving the raised lines of the artist's work. The block, fitted into the forme, would then have ink rolled onto its face and be printed with the rest of the page. This was the normal laborious way of making illustration blocks until the 1880s when the photographic process took over and the drawing was photographed onto the block. Finally the metal 'process' block was developed, onto which the picture was photographed and acid employed to eat away the white parts, leaving raised the black lines. Only then did readers see the artist's work first-hand.

The half page illustration made its appearance as a cartoon (the word had come to mean any amusing drawing) in its own right, in *Punch* at least, in 1845 – a drawing that could stand on its own two feet, separate and apart from the text on the rest of the page, and unconnected with any political comment on the national or world situation.

As with horsey and sporting humour (in which the world was divided strictly into us and them) angling wit too fell into separate and well defined categories. In early illustrations the fish (freshwater type) was often so much smarter than the fisherman; there were the Irish situations in which tyro anglers were told bigger lies than fish in the sea by sycophantic itinerant lake-dwellers, the Scottish ones that relied on the London businessman with the IQ of a minnow trying his hand for the first time and earning the undying contempt of his gillie – a variant of which was the drink joke in which the gillie's flask played a greater part than the rod and line.

Children rear their tousled little heads again and again of course. Small boys who know more than Uncle about the game, children who ask pertinent questions about a pastime which adults seem to sleep away; the girl-in-the-boat jokes, the fish-bites-man situations are seen, and the bored maiden who casts her line in an effort to lure the angler into deeper waters is sometimes daringly depicted.

Now again a full-page engraving, marine or piscatorial, with a message is seen – like this

Lady (*cheerfully, after blank day*). "THIS REMINDS ME OF THE OLD *PUNCH* STORY OF THE LUNATIC WHO LOOKED OVER THE ASYLUM WALL AND SAID TO A MAN WHO HAD BEEN FISHING FOR HOURS AND CAUGHT NOTHING, 'COME INSIDE.'"

Gillie (*after profound reflection*). "I'M THENKING, MEM, YON LUNATIC WAS NO A FESHERMAN."

Punch *perpetuates its own jokes.*

one that followed the laying of the second Atlantic Telegraph cable in 1865. With 'A Word to Mermaids' from Neptune it was accompanied by this verse:

Avast, there, nor swing on that cable,
You mischievous maidens avast!
And I'll tell you as well as I'm able,
Why that rope in the sea has been cast.

'Tis a link of electric connection
Between the New World and the Old;
'Twill strengthen each tie of affection,
Give each nation on each firmer hold.

Small fear of their fumbling or fighting
While they join hands thus under the seas;
While an instant will serve for the righting
Of any wrong heads that may be . . .

Doubt, distrust, envy, hatred, and malice.
All will vanish; peace, goodwill, appear;
So avast, there, you Polly and Alice,
And mind that'ere cable's kept clear!

. . . simple, pleasant sentiments on the relationship between Britain and the USA, ninety years

"I'M TRYING TO PUT HIM BACK—HE'S A BIT UNDER WEIGHT FOR THIS RIVER."

Fishing humour, freshwater category.

after the first relationship started to break up . . .

Amongst the fishing humour there was of course much seaside fun, particularly when little Jimmy caught a crab with his net or his toe, but sea fishing was depicted in a very different light from that halcyon freshwater occupation with rod and line. Here the wicked humour of the artist limns clapped hand to mouth in a vain effort to stem the sea-green surge of nausea, and has the hearty boatman comment on the long hours of sailing time left before the beloved shore is reached.

Curates? We must have curates in piscatorial situations for they seem to appear in every other walk of life in the cartoon world (more a myth than a fact, this) and indeed the occasional cleric is seen admonishing a diminutive and usually ragged angler who has not the slightest intention of acting upon his dictum.

Most political cartoons of the past are meaningless today. Political gambits involving Messrs C*mpb*l B*nnerm*n and A. J. B*lfo*r and later the vociferous and very Celtic Ll*yd G*org* pop in and out of the pages, sometimes in tense marine situations, but the fire that inspired the illustrations has been ashes for many years. Just one we noticed – it could have referred to the Cod War.

Through the hardships of two world wars and the dangers of two peacetimes in between, the steadfast angler has sat on his bank in tranquillity, indulging in his ancient pastime – occasionally grumbling about the noisy shells that could disturb his fish, or irritated at hooking a mine instead of a bass. And the pages of today's humorous press show no diminution of the interest in fishy jokes, although one sometimes sees a resurrected ancient in modern dress. However there is a strictly limited number of ways to tickle out laughter and, like Izaac Walton, today's illustrators are not to be criticised for a little genuine research into past pages of piscatorial fun. . .

Fishing, now the largest participant sport in Great Britain, can be a shoulder-to-shoulder contest, or can be taken in Waltonian solitude still. Take this book with you to either type of venue. But don't smile too loudly.

THE HARVEST OF THE SEA.

FATHER NEPTUNE. "THERE'S PLENTY FOR EVERYBODY!—HUMPH!—IF YOU COULD ONLY *GATHER IT!*"

1837-1850

Enter the poacher . . . the infant Prince of Wales – goldfish-bowl angler, early Victorian bedbugs and those wordless paragraph-separators.

TRUTH STRANGER THAN FICTION.

Professional Poacher. "PRAPS YOU EIN'T AWEER, YOUNG GEN'LEMAN, THAT THIS HERE BIT O' WATER IS STRICKLY PERSERVED."

FISHING OFF BRIGHTON.

"O yes! It's very easy to say 'Catch hold of him!'"

ROYAL SPORT.

It will be in the recollection of our readers that a handsome rod (which turns out to be really a fishing-rod after all), was a little while ago presented to the Prince of Wales. His Royal Highness has lately had some capital sport with this rod, having succeeded in capturing several of his Mamma's gold fish, one of which was as big as a dace and weighed six ounces. It was very nearly pulling the Prince in.

TRIUMPHANT SUCCESS OF MR. BRIGGS.

Somehow or other (assisted by his Little Boy Walter), he catches a Jack, which, to use Mr. B.'s own words, Flies at him, and Barks like a Dog!

OUR FRIEND, 'ARRY BELVILLE, IS SO KNOCKED ALL OF A HEAP BY THE BEAUTY OF THE FOREIGN FISH GIRLS, THAT HE OFFERS HIS 'AND AND 'ART TO THE LOVELY PAULINE.

MOST UNACCOUNTABLE.

"CONFOUND THAT URCHIN! HERE HAVE I BEEN FLOGGING AWAY ALL DAY, AND NOT EVEN CAUGHT SO MUCH AS A TITTLEBAT."

OH! WHAT A SURPRISE!

MR. BOBKINS BAITS HIS TRIMMERS OVER-NIGHT WITH SOME FINE LIVELY FROGS, AND FINDS IN THE MORNING THAT THEY OBJECT TO BECOME FOOD FOR FISHES.

BOTTOM FISHING.

Piscator No. 1 (*miserably*). "NOW, TOM, *DO* LEAVE OFF. IT IS'NT OF ANY USE AND IT'S GETTING QUITE DARK."

Piscator No. 2. "LEAVE OFF!! WHAT A PRECIOUS DISAGREEABLE CHAP YOU ARE! YOU COME OUT FOR A DAY'S PLEASURE, AND YOU'RE ALWAYS A WANTING TO GO HOME!"

FLY-FISHING. A NICE RIPPLE ON THE WATER.—"*NOW FOR A BIG ONE!*"

COMMON OBJECTS AT THE SEA-SIDE.

Boy. "Oh! look here, Ma! I've caught a Fish just like those thingamies in my Bed at our Lodgings!"

PATIENCE REWARDED.

Piscator. "A-hah! Got you at last, have I?—and a fine Week's Trouble I've had to catch you!"

MANNERS · AND · CVSTOMS · OF · Ye · ENGLYSHE IN 1849. No 25.

Ye. SPORT · OF · PVNTE · FYSHYNGE · OFF RYCHMONDE

Knobbles, Jun. hears that the later you fish in an evening, the more likely you are to catch something. He never tries it again.

A DAY'S FISHING AND A RUN WITH A FRIEND'S HOUND.

Owner of Attached Quadruped (frantically). "LET HIM GO! GIVE HIM LINE! HOLD ON! TAKE CARE! I'M COMING WITH THE LANDING-NET!"

ANGLING IN THE SERPENTINE.—SATURDAY P.M.

Piscator, No. 1. "HAD EVER A BITE, JIM?"
Piscator, No. 2. "NOT YET—I ONLY COME HERE LAST WEDNESDAY!"

Piscatorial Leech

John Leech, perhaps the greatest of the early Victorian line illustrators, was more at home in the hunting field, but his essays into the marine world have a charm of their own, and his simple portrayal of contemporary figures have a ring of truth.

ROMANCE AND REALITY.

Beautiful Being (who is all soul). "HOW GRAND, HOW SOLEMN, DEAR FREDERICK, THIS IS! I REALLY THINK THE OCEAN IS MORE BEAUTIFUL UNDER THIS ASPECT THAN UNDER ANY OTHER!"

Frederick (who has about as much poetry in him as a Codfish). "HM—AH! YES. PER-WAPS. BY THE WAY, BLANCHE—THERE'S A FELLA SWIMPING S'POSE WE ASK HIM IF HE CAN GET US SOME PWAWNS FOR BWEAKFAST TO-MOWAW MORNING?"

A GOOD SIZED FLOAT.

Little Gent (with undue familiarity). "I SAY, MY OLD COCKYWAX,—I S'POSE THE FISH AIN'T VERY LARGE OFF RAMSGIT—ARE THEY!"

Fisherman. "WELL! I SHOULDN'T SAY AS THEY WAS WERRY SMALL—WHEN WE'RE OBLIGED TO USE SICH FLOATS AS THEM TO OUR FISHIN' TACKLE! MY YOUNG COCKYWAX!" *(Gent is shut up.)*

THE GOLD FISH AT HAMPTON COURT.

ANGLERS HEAR STRANGE THINGS.

Piscator. "ARE THERE ANY BARBEL ABOUT HERE, GOV'NOR?"
Host. "ANY BARBEL ABOUT HERE!! I SHOULD RAYTHER THINK THERE WAS A FEW. HERE'S THE PICTUR O' WUN MY LITTLE BOY KETCHED JUST HOPPOSIT."

1850-1860

Neptune holds court, the saga of Mr Briggs (a popular figure of fun in *Punch* and almost always in sporting difficulties), the pleasures of the early season.

NOT LIKELY.

"I'LL PUNCH YOUR 'EAD, DIRECTLY, IF YOU DON'T LEAVE ORFF. HOW DO YER THINK THE WHAT'S-A-NAMES 'LL BITE, IF YOU KEEP ON A SPLASHIN' LIKE THAT?"

HOW VERY KIND!

Knowing Old Hand (who evidently does NOT want to keep the best of the water to himself). "DON'T YOU THINK, MY DEAR FELLOW, YOU HAD BETTER FISH FROM THE OTHER SIDE, AND THEN WE SHALL BE LESS LIKELY TO INTERFERE WITH EACH OTHER."

A WORD TO THE MERMAIDS.

NEPTUNE. "AHO-O-O-O-OY, THERE! GET OFF O' THAT 'ERE CABLE, CAN'T YER—THAT'S THE WAY T'OTHER ONE WAS WRECKED!!!"

FLY-FISHING.

MR. BUNGLE ALWAYS MAKES HIS FLIES ON THE BANK OF THE STREAM. HERE IS ONE OF HIS MOST SUCCESSFUL EFFORTS.

MR. BRIGGS'S PLEASURES OF FISHING.

MR. BRIGGS, ANXIOUS TO BECOME A "COMPLETE ANGLER," STUDIES THE "GENTLE ART" OF FLY-FISHING

HE IS HERE SUPPOSED TO BE GETTING HIS TACKLE IN ORDER, AND TRYING THE MANAGEMENT OF HIS LINE

MR. B. AS HE APPEARED FROM SIX IN THE MORNING UNTIL THREE IN THE AFTERNOON, WHEN——

HAVING HOOKED A "FISH," HE IS LANDED TO PLAY IT. THE FISH RUNS AWAY WITH HIM—AND MR. B. IS DRAGGED ABOUT A MILE AND A HALF OVER WHAT HE CONSIDERS A RATHER DIFFICULT COUNTRY.

ON ARRIVING AT "HELL'S HOLE," HE IS DETAINED FOR THREE-QUARTERS OF AN HOUR, WHILE THE FISH SULKS AT THE BOTTOM.——

THE FISH HAVING REFRESHED HIMSELF, AND RECOVERED HIS SPIRITS, BOLTS AGAIN WITH MR. B.

AFTER A LONG AND EXCITING STRUGGLE, MR. B. IS ON THE POINT OF LANDING HIS PRIZE, WHEN—THE LINE UNFORTUNATELY BREAKS!

HOWEVER, IN MUCH LESS TIME THAN IT HAS TAKEN TO MAKE THIS IMPERFECT SKETCH—ACCOUTRED AS HE IS—HE PLUNGES IN—AND AFTER A DESPERATE ENCOUNTER, HE SECURES A MAGNIFICENT SALMON, FOR WHICH HE DECLARES HE WOULD NOT TAKE A GUINEA A POUND!—AND IT IS NOW STUFFED IN THE GLASS-CASE OVER THE ONE WHICH CONTAINS HIS LATE FAVOURITE SPOTTED HUNTER.

THE GENTLE CRAFT.

Contemplative Man (in punt). "I DON'T SO MUCH CARE ABOUT THE SPORT. IT'S THE DELICIOUS REPOSE I ENJOY SO."

THAMES FISHING.

Fisherman (to Old Gentleman). "THEY'RE A' BITIN' AWAY OVER 'ERE, SIR! JUST STEP ACROSS THAT THERE BIT O' WOOD, SIR, AND YOU'LL HAVE A CAPITAL PITCH, SIR!"

Old Gentleman. "ACROSS THAT BIT OF WOOD! DOES THE MAN THINK I'M A ROPE-DANCER?"

THANK GOODNESS! FLY-FISHING HAS BEGUN!

Miller. "DON'T THEY, REALLY! PERHAPS THEY'LL RISE BETTER TOWARDS THE COOL OF THE EVENING THEY MOSTLY DO!"

Eternal Youth

Two cynics, an innocent with advanced ideas – and an Alice in 'Through the Looking-Glass' mood.

"NOT PROVEN."

Presbyterian Minister. "DON'T YOU KNOW IT'S WICKED TO CATCH FISH ON THE SAWBATH!?"
Small Boy (not having had a rise all the Morning). "WHA'S CATCHIN' FESH?!"

A GREAT FIND.

"OH!! LOOK'EE HERE, SIR, HERE'S A WARM LONG ENOUGH TO LAST YOU A FORTNIGHT."

Nervous Small Boy. "PLEASE, DO YOU ALLOW MIXED SHRIMPING?"

MENACE.

Little Angler (to her refractory Bait). "KEEP STILL, YOU TIRESOME LITTLE THING! IF YOU DON'T LEAVE OFF SKRIGGLING, I'LL THROW YOU AWAY, AND TAKE ANOTHER!"

1860-1880

Imperial heyday; conversation pieces on the shore, linguistic comment, lucky diver, Scottish humour becomes decipherable, and the gillie appears.

"BLOW FLY FISHING."

THIS IS HOW OLD PUFFINS (WITH THE AID OF A BLOW-TUBE) GETS OVER THE EXERTION OF THROWING A FLY.

IRISH LAKE-FISHING.

Mr. Briggs. "BUT THE BOAT SEEMS VERY LEAKY, AND TO WANT MENDING A GOOD DEAL."

Boatman. "WANT MENDIN' IS IT? OH, NIVER FEAR! SHURE THE BOAT'S WELL ENOUGH. IF YE SIT STILL, AND DON'T COFF OR SNAZE, SHE'LL CARRY YE PRETTY WELL!"

THE GENTLE CRAFTSMAN. (P)

Irascible Angler (who hasn't had a rise all day). "THERE!"—*(Throwing his fly-book into the stream, with a malediction)*—"TAKE YOUR CHOICE!"

"SMALL MERCIES."

First Jolly Angler (with empty Creel). "WELL, WE'VE HAD A VERY PLEASANT DAY! WHAT A DELIGHTFUL PURSUIT IT IS!"

Second Ditto (with ditto). "GLORIOUS! I SHAN'T FORGET THAT NIBBLE WE HAD JUST AFTER LUNCH, AS LONG AS I LIVE!"

Both. "AH!!"

A LIKELY BAIT.

Piscator. "OHO! THIS IS THE PLACE WHERE THE BIG TROUT ARE, IS IT? THEN THIS IS THE SORT OF *FLY*, I THINK!"

LINGUA EAST ANGLIA.

First Angler (to Country Boy). "I SAY, MY LAD, JUST GO TO MY FRIEND ON THE BRIDGE THERE, AND SAY I SHOULD BE MUCH OBLIGED TO HIM IF HE'D SEND ME SOME BAIT."

Country Boy (to Second Angler, in the Eastern Counties language). "THA' THERE BO' SAHY HE WANT A WURRUM!!"

ENCOURAGING PROSPECT!

Piscator Juvenis. "ANY SPORT, SIR?"
Piscator Senex. "OH, YES; VERY GOOD SPORT."
Piscator Juvenis. "BREAM?"
Piscator Senex. "NO!"
Piscator Juvenis. "PERCH?"
Piscator Senex. "NO!"
Piscator Juvenis. "WHAT SPORT, THEN?"
Piscator Senex. "WHY, KEEPING CLEAR OF THE WEEDS!"

THE DIVER IN SEARCH OF THE ATLANTIC CABLE GETS INTO HOT WATER.

"NO FEAR."

Fisherman. "Take care, Donald—You'll be Drowned!"

Donald. "Trooned!—in a Dub like thus! If I was, I'd be ashamed to show my Face in Oban again!"

COUSINLY AFFECTION.

Jim (who has taken his Cousin Jack-fishing for the first time). "Now, Tom, just put your Finger in, and Loosen that Fourth Hook."

SALMON FISHING.

Piscator. "Follow him up! It's all very well to say Follow him up!"

QUITE IN LUCK'S WAY.

"AN UNCOMMONLY LIKELY PLACE, THAT, FOR A JACK, UNDERNEATH THE WILLOWS THERE; AND WHAT'S MORE, I DON'T THINK ANY ONE HAS BEEN HERE THIS MORNING TO DISTURB THE WATER."

MECHANICS IN SPORT.

No. 2.—Steam Ejector and Spinning Apparatus for Jack and Chub Fishing.

AWFUL EFFECT OF FISHING ON THE HUMAN MIND.

PHERKINS. "*It has occurred to me, Sam, that throwing in Ground Bait is nothing more or less than—as it were—a species of Advertising!*"

SCOTCH 'SALMODY.

WE LEARN FROM THE *INVERNESS COURIER* OF THE INVENTION OF A NEW ROCKET POP GUN, WITH WHICH A DISTINGUISHED SPORTSMAN (THE INVENTOR) HAS DONE GREAT EXECUTION ON THE SALMON IN THE HIGHLAND RIVERS WHEN THEY WON'T TAKE A FLY!

"NOT SO FAST!"

Old Gent (soliloquising, in the Wilds of Glenmuchie). "AH, WELL, THIS IS VERY JOLLY! WEALTH'S A GREAT BLESSING NOT THAT I'M A RICH MAN—BUT AFTER THE TURMOIL AND WORRY OF BUSINESS, TO BE ABLE TO RETIRE TO THESE CHARMING SOLITUDES, THE SILENCE ONLY BROKEN BY THE GRATEFUL SOUNDS OF THE RIPPLING STREAM ('BURN,' I MEAN. AH! I NEARLY HAD HIM THEN!), AND THE HUM OF THE BEE! TO BE ABLE TO LEAVE LONDON AND ITS TIRESOME MILLIONS, AND FORGET ALL THE LOW –"

Voice from the Bridge (the ubiquitous "'Arry"). 'COULD YER 'BLIGE US WITH A WORM, GOV-NOUR?"!!

"PHYSICAL GEOGRAPHY."

English Angler (on this side of the Tweed). "HI, DONALD! COME OVER AND HELP ME TO LAND HIM—A 20-POUNDER I'LL SWEAR——"

Highlander (on the other). "IT WULL TAK' YE A LANG TIME TO LAN' THAT FUSH TOO, D'YE KEN, SIR, WHATEVER!—YE HAE HEUKET THE KINGDOM O' AULD SCOTLAND!"

Female Line

Charmers who set out to hook more than trout, sportsmen who get in a tangle, and a Charlie who hooks a mate.

WARM WORK.

Fly Fishing is a gentle Pastime, exercising the Mind without fatiguing the Body. Yet here we have a Gentleman in a sad state of heat and flurry from merely setting up this Young Lady's Rod!

Mother. "HOW ARE YOU GETTING ON, NEDDY? HAVE YOU HAD ANY SPORT?"
Boy. "WELL, MA, WE HAVEN'T CAUGHT ANY FISH, BUT WE'VE DROWNED SEVERAL WORMS!"

Mrs. Brown. "WELL, I MUST BE GOING IN A MINUTE."
Mr. B. "WHAT FOR?"
Mrs. B. "WHY, I FORGOT TO ORDER THE FISH FOR DINNER."

PROVERBS (PICTORIALLY PUT).

"It's an ill wind," etc.

Particularly when it brings about a serious entanglement between Charlie's Line and Maudie's pretty Hair. [*Charlie is very short-sighted, so he says.*

SOMETHING LIKE A CATCH.

Mrs. Binks (sick of it). "REALLY, JOHN! HOW CAN YOU BEAR TO SPEND YOUR TIME WHIP—WHIP—WHIPPING AT THE STREAM ALL DAY LONG, AND NEVER A SINGLE FISH TAKING THE LEAST NOTICE OF YOU?"

John. "AH, BUT THINK O' THE DELIGHT, MARIA, WHEN YOU DO GET A FISH! LOR' BLESS US, MY DEAR, HAVE YOU FORGOTTEN THE DAY WHEN YOU HOOKED ME?"

AMENITIES OF THE "GENTLE CRAFT."

"Be *Tender* with him, Miss! *Be Tender!*"

1880-1900

Rivals for the late Victorian humorist – *Judy* and *Fun* – tell the fishing tale. Aimed at a more simple level (e.g. A Wigged Tale, and A Fly Fisher) both *Fun* and *Judy* found a readership strong enough to keep them afloat for some thirty years.

HAPPY THOUGHT.
HOW TO EQUALISE THE ODDS!

HEARD ON THE THAMES TOW-PATH.

Active Nephew (loudly).—"You've got a bite, uncle!"
Lazy Avuncular Relative (testily).—"Yes, I know I have; but that's no reason why you should wake me up just as I was having a comfortable doze. Worst thing about fishing is that one does get a bite sometimes. Confounded good mind to clout your head!"

"WALTON'S COMPLETE BUNGLER."
"CONFOUND IT!—AND THE FISH RISING SO NICELY!"

English Tourist. "HOW EVER DO YOU KEEP WARM WADING LIKE THAT THIS WEATHER?"
Old Scot. "WHUSKEY, NAETHING BUT WHUSKEY! I JUST TAK' A BOTTLE A DAY. MAN, IT'S GRAND FOR THE CIRCULATION. MY WIFE SAYS WHEN I PIT MY HEAD IN THE WATER IN THE MORNING, SHE CAN HEAR IT FIZZLE!"

ANOTHER FISHING STORY.

Away to the river

"Well, no, sir. Fishin' ain't allowed, but if you tips me 'arf a crown, you can fish for ten moile down this 'ere bank for what I care

(Thankee, sir), 'Cause yer see it ain't got nothin' at all to do wi' me!"

The cast

The catch

The can-can of triumph

The Keeper

Homeward

Subsequent amazing growth of the fish at the Ananias Fishing Club.

"My mother bids me bind my hair," sang the sweetest of her sex; and then her dearest bosom friend answered, kindly, "That I should, and put it away for a time in your drawer, for those dyed plaits soon get off colour if you keep them too much in the sun." And after this who can say that a woman can't have friends.

The man who wanted to write a sonnet to his mistress's eyebrows has since changed his mind. He's going to paint a picture of 'em, and call it "A Symphony in Black and White"; for there's enough ink and pearl powder about them to set up Mr. Whistler for a sensational study of Chelsea Bridge.

MISPLACED SYMPATHY.

"WELL? HAVE YOU CAUGHT ANY FISH, BILLY?"

"WELL, I *REALLY* CAUGHT *TWO!* BUT THEY WERE QUITE YOUNG, POOR LITTLE THINGS, AND SO THEY *DIDN'T KNOW HOW TO HOLD ON!*"

THE METROPOLIS IN AUGUST 1888.

FORESEEN AND DRAWN BY OUR ARTIST (THE MELANCHOLY AND LEFT-ALL-ALONE-IN-LONDON ONE), AFTER A SOLITARY SUPPER AT THE "PORK-PIE CLUB," COLD HARBOUR LANE.

[*Happily Our Artist's dyspeptic Forecast has been falsified.*

PRECAUTIONS.

Saxon Angler (to his Keeper). "YOU SEEM IN A GREAT HURRY WITH YOUR CLIP! I HAVEN'T SEEN A SIGN OF A FISH YET—NOT A RISE!"

Duncan. "'DEED, SIR, I WISNA A BOTHERIN' MYSEL' ABOOT THE FUSH; BUT SEEIN' YOU WIS NEW TO THE BUSINESS, I HAD A THOCHT IT WIDNA BE LANG AFORE YOU WERE NEEDIN' A LEFT OOT O' THE WATTER YOURSEL'!"

AT THE FOUNTAIN-HEAD.

ALMOST BEFORE SHE KNOWS WHERE SHE IS, AND BY A MERE NOD OF HER HEAD, THRIFTY LITTLE MRS. MILDMAY BECOMES THE OWNER OF SIX SPLENDID COD, A DOZEN FINE BLACK-JACK, AND FOURTEEN MAGNIFICENT SKATE, —ALL FOR THE RIDICULOUSLY SMALL SUM OF HALF-A-CROWN. SHE SUDDENLY REMEMBERS THAT HER YOUNG FAMILY CAN'T BEAR FISH, AND THAT HER HUSBAND HAS BEEN FORBIDDEN TO EAT IT!

TABLE MANNERS.

Father Pelican (reprovingly). "HOW CAN YOU EXPECT TO SPEAK DISTINCTLY WITH YOUR MOUTH FULL?"

FUBLEIGH, HAVING ACCIDENTALLY HOOKED A FINE, ACTIVE JACK SHEEP, WHICH WAS GRAZING ON THE BANK BEHIND HIM, HAS (IN THE ENDEAVOUR TO SAVE HIS TACKLE) QUITE THE BEST SPORT OF THE SEASON WITH THE MAY-FLY.

THE OPTIMIST.

Meek Visitor. "ANY LUCK TO-DAY?"
Gruff Angler (who has caught nothing). "YES THANKS! I HAD A CAPITAL BREAKFAST OF HAM AND EGGS!"

EXPLAINED.

Keeper. "DO YOU KNOW THIS WATER IS PRESERVED, SIR?"
Angler (of little experience, still awaiting a bite). "I THOUGHT THERE WAS SOMETHING THE MATTER WITH IT!"

A HAPPY ENTANGLEMENT.

Whether it was by Accident or Design, nobody can tell, but her Lines got inextricably mixed with his, while Angling in a Highland Stream—and now they are engaged to be Married!

"THE OLD ADAM."

The Minister (coming on them unawares). "E-e-h! Sandy McDougal! Ah'm sorry to see this! And you too, Wully! Fishin' o' the Sawbath! Ah thoucht ah'd enstellet better Prenciples——" *(A Rise.)* "E-e-eh! Wully, Man!—ye hae 'm!—it's entil 'm! Haud up yer R-rod, Man—or ye'll lose 'm—tak' car-r-re!——" [*Recollects himself, and walks off.*

A TALE OF A FISH.
1
They sat there side by side every day fishing amicably and catching nothing. But after forty years Worm-washer, who was always impatient began to brood
2.
And in the evening when they met as usual at the inn, to smoke and lie to each other about great catches he still pondered moodily, apart
3.
Next morning, when they came to their daily camp, he was there before them. with a weird brightness in his eye, and he had caught a great perch.
4
The day after he caught another, and s
on for many succeeding days. He became famous. His name was in the local paper
5.
But one day an accident happened to his daily great fish and all the newspaper and straw it was stuffed with came out, as he was bearing it off in triumph.
6.
When he next came back he found the tail of it still there.
An after that somehow he never had another bite.

AGGRAVATING.

(Poor Jones has been whipping the stream all day without a rise.)

Hieland Laddie.—"They're best fryet in butter, sir!"

Hieland Lassie.—"Ye micht gie's a' ye canna eat yersel', sir!"

Hieland Laddie.—"Wull a come owre an' cairry them hame for ye, sir?"

THE HUMOURS OF ANGLING.

Piscatorial Cockney.—"'Give him the line!' Why, hang it all, he's gone off with it, and the hook into the bargain."

Sandy McAlister.—"Dinna sweir, mon, dinna sweir! It's on'y to be expeckit that a fish in the watter wad get the better of a fule off the laend."

A WIGGED TALE.

THEODOSIUS HEELTAPS was a masher of the mashers, and Miss Whalebone worshipped the very ground he trod on, but especially did she dote on this callow young man's waving ringlets, the admired of all admirers.

Hold, rash youth! what fiendish fate ever prompted thee to go fooling about where the sportive anglers most do congregate?

What she said was: "Hence, ridiculous impostor! and never let me set eyes on such a fright again!" The hapless Theodosius is missing at Lloyd's.

Boy (to Piscator, who has been whipping the stream all day without any luck). YOU'LL BE GETTING A FISH CAUGHT ON ONE OF THEM LITTLE 'OOKS *IF YER AIN'T CAREFUL.*

CURATE: "*Cruel boy! Are you trying to catch those poor little minnows?*"
BOY: "*No, sir, the big 'uns!*"

A ROMANCE IN TWO CHAPTERS.

CHAPTER I.

THE FIRST TIME GEORGE AND MARY MET WAS AT MRS. DIXON'S GARDEN-PARTY, AT PUTNEY. AN OLD GENTLEMAN WAS FISHING. ALL SHE SAID WAS, "HE DOESN'T SEEM TO BE CATCHING ANY FISH." GEORGE ONLY ANSWERED, "TRUE HAPPINESS LIES IN ANTICIPATION." SHE THOUGHT HE MUST HAVE AN ORIGINAL MIND, AND SECRETLY LOVED HIM.

CHAPTER II.

THEIR NEXT MEETING WAS AT THE SAME PLACE, UNDER THE SAME CIRCUMSTANCES. THE SAME OLD GENTLEMAN WAS FISHING. "HE DOESN'T SEEM TO BE CATCHING ANY FISH," SAID GEORGE. "TRUE HAPPINESS LIES IN ANTICIPATION," SAID MARY. "WHAT AN ORIGINAL MIND!" THOUGHT GEORGE, AND HE FELL IN LOVE WITH HER. [*They are now Married!*

Note.—The above sketch conveys its own lesson, and we should be guilty of attempting to *lessen* our own responsibility in the matter were we to omit a single detail, each of which is of suf-*fish*ient interest.

Papa, Maman, et Bébé s'en vont à la Pêche aux Crevettes.

CONSCIENTIOUS FLATTERY.

Boatman. "I canna mind a finer Fesh for its size!"

FAUTE DE MIEUX.

Constance. "CAUGHT ANY FISH, ARCHIE?" *Archie.* "NO—NONE."
Constance. "HAD ANY BITES?" *Archie.* "YES—HUNDREDS."
Constance. "TROUT?" *Archie.* "NO—MIDGES!"

BETTER LATE THAN NEVER.

Boy (on the stump, who has been patiently watching the strange angler for about an hour). YOU AIN'T CAUGHT ANYTHING, 'AVE YER!

Stranger. NO, NOT YET, MY BOY.

Boy. THERE WASN'T NO WATER IN THAT POND, TILL IT RAINED LAST NIGHT.

Any one can fish in this Water barrin thim as have Payd for a Licinse

"NO RINT!"

SAXON SUBSCRIBER (TO AN IRISH "FISHERY") READS NOTICE-BOARD! TABLEAU!

THE MISSING LETTER.

Angler (after landing his tenth—reading notice). "THE MAN WHO WROTE THAT SIGN COULDN'T HAVE BEEN USING THE RIGHT BAIT!"

HARD TO PLEASE.

Piscator, Senior. "WHAT! YER WANT TO CHUCK IT UP JUS' BECAUSE WE NEVER CATCHES NOTHING. WHY, I'D LIKE TO KNOW HOW YER PROPOSES TO SPEND THE REMAINDER OF YER 'OLIDAYS, EH?"

BUMPSTEAD says:—

"Never care for female cackle!
Angler's heaven is heaps of Tackle!"

But BUMPSTEAD is a bachelor.

Third Entry.—Have been reading books and studying tackle, till I'm half dazed. Am in great fog about baits, make an awful

mess of mounting a line; my teeth ache with biting "shots" on to the "gut," and my fingers—not to name other parts of my person—are sore from fortuitous hook-pricks. I never knew any-

CUTTING.

Big Scotchman. "CONFOUND THESE MIDGES!"
Little Cockney "WHY, THEY 'AVEN'T TOUCHED ME!"
Big Scotchman. "MAYBE THEY HAVENA NOTICED YE YET!"

HE COULDN'T SEE THE POINT OF IT AT ALL!

A GENTLE HINT.

Mr. Giglamps (who has been caught by Keeper with some fish in his basket under taking size). "OH—ER—WELL, YOU SEE, FACT IS, MY GLASSES —ER—MAGNIFY A GOOD DEAL. MAKE THINGS LOOK LARGER THAN THEY REALLY ARE!"

Keeper (about to receive smaller Tip than meets the occasion). "AH! MAKES YER PUT DOWN A SHILLIN' WHEN YER MEANS 'ALF-A-CROWN, SOMETIMES, I DESSAY, SIR!"

LATEST FROM DOTTYVILLE.

Lunatic (suddenly popping his head over wall). "WHAT ARE YOU DOING THERE?
Brown. "FISHING."
Lunatic. "CAUGHT ANYTHING?"
Brown. "NO."
Lunatic. "HOW LONG HAVE YOU BEEN THERE?"
Brown. "SIX HOURS."
Lunatic. "COME *INSIDE*!"

THE LAY OF A SUCCESSFUL ANGLER.

THE dainty artificial fly
Designed to catch the wily trout,
Full loud *laudabunt alii*,
And I will join, at times, no doubt,
But yet my praise, without pretence,
Is not from great experience.

I talk as well as anyone
About the different kinds of tackle,
I praise the Gnat, the Olive Dun,
Discuss the worth of wings and hackle;
I've flies myself of each design,
No book is better filled than mine.

But when I reach the river's side
Alone, for none of these I wish,
No victim to a foolish pride,
My object is to capture fish;
Let me confess, then, since you ask it—
A worm it is which fills my basket!

O brown, unlovely, wriggling worm,
On which with scorn the haughty look,
It is thy fascinating squirm
Which brings the fattest trout to book,
From thee unable to refrain,
Though flies are cast for him in vain!

Deep gratitude to thee I feel,
And then, perhaps, it's chiefly keen,
When rival anglers view my creel,
And straightway turn a jealous green;
And, should they ask me—"What's your fly?"
"A fancy pattern," I reply!

SUPERB.

Podgson (a recently joined disciple of the gentle craft). "AH, NOW I FLATTER MYSELF THAT I PLAYED THAT FELLOW WITH CONSIDERABLE SKILL, AND LANDED HIM WITHOUT THE NET, TOO!"

QUITE A LITTLE PARABLE.

The Rector (returning from day's fishing—in reply to usual question). "SPORT? OH! WRETCHED!! WRETCHED!!! TRIED EVERY DODGE I COULD THINK OF, BUT NOTHING WOULD TEMPT 'EM."

Canny Scot (who rather suspects the Rector of a fondness for good living). "A—WEEL RECTHOR, NA DOOT THEY SET SOME ON US A POORFUL EXAMPLE I' NO GIVIN' WAY TO THEIR CARNAL PROCLEEVITIES, AND REFUSIN' TO BE TA'EN IN BY THE FA'SE BLANDISHMENTS O' THE DEEVIL, I' THE SHAPE O' YER AWN ARTIFEECIAL FLEES."

CONFESSIONS OF A DUFFER.

VII.—THE DUFFER WITH A SALMON-ROD.

No pursuit is more sedentary, if one may talk of a sedentary pursuit, and none more to my taste, than trout-fishing as practised in the South of England. Given fine weather, and a good novel, nothing can be more soothing than to sit on a convenient stump, under a willow, and watch the placid kine standing in the water, while the brook murmurs on, and perhaps the kingfisher flits to and fro. Here you sit and fleet the time carelessly, till a trout rises. Then, indeed, duty demands that you shall crawl in the manner of the serpent till you come within reach of him, and cast a fly, which usually makes him postpone his dinner-hour. But he will come on again, there is no need for you to change your position, and you can always fill your basket easily—with irises and marsh-marigolds.

Such are our county contents, but woe befall the day when I took to salmon-fishing. The outfit is expensive, "half-crown flees" soon mount up, especially if you never go out without losing your fly-book. If you buy a light rod, say of fourteen feet, the chances are that it will not cover the water, and a longer rod requires in the fisherman the strength of a Sandow. You need wading-breeches, which come up nearly to the neck, and weigh a couple of stone. The question has been raised, can one swim in them, in case of an accident? For *one*, I can answer, he can't. The reel is about the size of a butter-keg, the line measures hundreds of yards, and the place where you fish for salmon is usually at the utter ends of the earth. Some enthusiasts begin in February. Covered with furs, they sit in the stern of a boat, and are pulled in a funereal manner up and down Loch Tay, while the rods fish for themselves. The angler's only business is to pick them up if a salmon bites, and when this has gone on for a few days, with no bite, Influenza, or a hard frost with curling, would be rather a relief. This kind of thing is not really angling, and a Duffer is as good at it as an expert.

Real difficulties and sufferings begin when you reach the Cruach-na-spiel-bo, which sounds like Gaelic, and will serve us as a name for the river. It is, of course, extremely probable that you pay a large rent for the right to gaze at a series of red and raging floods, or at a pale and attenuated trickle of water, murmuring peevishly through a drought. But suppose, for the sake of argument, that the water is "in order," and only running with deep brown swirls at some thirty miles an hour. Suppose also, a large presumption, that the Duffer does not leave any indispensable part of his equipment at home. He arrives at the stream, and as he detests a gillie, whose contempt for the Duffer breeds familiarity, he puts up his rod, selects a casting line, knots on the kind of fly which is locally recommended, and steps into the water. Oh, how cold it is! I begin casting at the top of the stream, and step from a big boulder into a hole. Stagger, stumble, violent bob forwards, recovery, trip up, and here one is in a sitting position in the bed of the stream. However, the high india-rubber breeks have kept the water out, except about a pailful, which gradually illustrates the equilibrium of fluids in the soles of one's stockings. However, I am on my feet again, and walking more gingerly, though to the spectator, my movements suggest partial intoxication. That is because the bed of the stream is full of boulders, which one cannot see, owing to the darkness of the water. There was a fish rose near the opposite side. My heart is in my mouth. I wade in as far as I can, and make a tremendous swipe with the rod. A frantic tug behind, crash, there goes the top of the rod! I am caught up in the root of a pine-tree, high up on the bank at my back. No use in the language of imprecation. I waddle out, climb the bank, extricate the fly, get out a spare top, and to work again, more cautiously. Something wrong, the hook has caught in my coat, between my shoulders. I must get the coat off somehow, not an easy thing to do, on account of my india-rubber armour. It is off at last. I cut the hook out with a knife making a big hole in the coat, and cast again. That was over him! I let the fly float down, working it scientifically. No response. Perhaps better look at the fly. Just my luck, I have cracked it off!

"I wade in as far as I can, and make a tremendous swipe with the rod."

Where is the fly-book? Where indeed? A feverish search for the fly-book follows—no use: it is not in the basket, it is not in my pocket; must have fallen out when I fell into the river. No good in looking for it, the water is too thick, I *thought* I heard a splash. Luckily there are some flies in my cap, it looks knowing to have some flies in one's cap, and it is not so easy to lose a cap, without noticing it, as to lose most things. Here is a big Silver Doctor that may do as the water is thick. I put one on, and begin again casting over where that fish rose. By George, there he came at me, at least I think it must have been at me, a great dark swirl, "the purple wave bowed over it like a hill," but he never touched me. Give him five minutes law, the hook is sure to be well fastened on, need not bother looking at that again. Five minutes take a long time in passing, when you are giving a salmon a rest. Good times and bad times and all times pass, so here goes. It is correct to begin a good way above him and come down to him. I'm past him; no, there is a long heavy drag under water, I get the point up, he is off like a shot, while I stand in a rather stupid attitude, holding on. If I cannot get out and run down the bank, he has me at his mercy. I do stagger out, somehow, falling on my back, but keeping the point up with my right hand. No bones broken, but surely he is gone! I begin reeling up the line, with a heavy heart, and try to lift it out of the water. It won't come, he is here still, he has only doubled back. Hooray! Nothing so nice as being all alone when you hook a salmon. No gillie to scream out contradictory orders. He is taking it very easy, but suddenly he moves out a few yards, and begins jiggering, that is, giving a series of short heavy tugs. They say he is never well hooked, when he jiggers. The rod thrills unpleasantly in my hands, I wish he wouldn't do that. It is very disagreeable and makes me very nervous. Hullo! he is off again up-stream, the reel ringing like mad: he gets into the thin water at the top, and jumps high in the air. He is a monster. Hullo! what's that splash? The reel has fallen off, it was always loose, and has got into the water. How am I to act now? He is coming back like mad, and all the line is loose, and I can't reel up. I begin pulling at the line to bring up the reel, but the reel only lets the line out, and now he is off again, down stream this time, and I after him, and the line running out at both ends at once, and now my legs get entangled in it, it is twisted all round me. He runs again and jumps, the line comes back in my face, all slack, something has given. It is the hook, it was not knotted on firmly to start with. He flings himself out of the water once more to be sure that he is free, and I sit down and gnaw the reel. Had ever anybody such bad fortune, but it is just my luck!

I go back to the place where the reel fell in, and by pulling cautiously I extract it from the stream. It shan't come off again; I tie it on with the leather lace of one of my brogues. Then I reel up the slack, and put on another fly, out of my cap, a Popham. Then I fish down the rest of the pool. Near the edge, in the slower part of the water, there is a long slow draw, before I can lift the point of the rod, a salmon jumps high out of the water at me,—and is gone! I never struck him, was too much taken aback at the moment; did not expect him then. Thank goodness, the hook is not off this time.

The next stream is very deep, strong and narrow; the best chance is close in on my side. By Jove, here he is, he took almost beside the rock. He sails leisurely out into the strength of the stream, if he will come up, I can manage him, but if he goes down, the water is very swift and broken, there are big boulders, and then a sheer wall of rock difficult to pass in cold blood, and then the Big Pool.

PREHISTORIC PEEPS.

A NOCTURNE WHICH WOULD SEEM TO SHOW THAT "RESIDENTIAL FLATS" WERE NOT WHOLLY UNKNOWN EVEN IN PRIMEVAL TIMES!

ANTICIPATION.

Piscator (short-sighted; he had been trolling all day for a big Pike that lay in a hole about here). "QUICK, JARVIS—THE LANDING-NET—I'VE GOT HIM!"

Jarvis. "AH, SIR, IT'S ONLY AN OLD FRYIN'-PAN! BUT THAT WILL BE USEFUL, Y'KNOW, SIR, WHEN WE DO CATCH HIM!"

All at Sea

Walton said 'No man is born an angler.' Certainly no man is born a sea angler if these illustrations are to be believed.

MISSED.

Angus. "EH, MON, THAT WASS A SPLENDID COD! IF WE HAD GOTTEN THAT COD NOO, WE MICHT HA' BEEN HA'AIN' A DRAM."
Mr. Smith (from Glasgow). "INDEED, AND YE WOULD, ANGUS."
Bauldry. "MEBBE, MAISTER SMUTH, IF WE WAD HAVE HAD A DRAM AFORE YE WASS LETTIN' DOON YER LINE, WE MICHT HAVE GRAPPIT THAT MUCKLE FUSH."

"FISHIN' AN' CATCHIN' FISH IS, AS YER MIGHT SAY, SIR, TWO WERRY DIFFERENT THINGS."

Imperturbable Boatman. "HAUD UP YER ROD, MAN! YE HAVE 'M! YE HAVE 'M!"

FACT AND FICTION.

(After a desperate encounter with a conger-eel, which takes possession of the boat, Edwin persuades the monster to return to its element.)

Extract from Angelina's correspondence: "YESTERDAY EDWIN AND I CAUGHT A SPLENDID CONGER-EEL, BUT UNFORTUNATELY IT FELL OVERBOARD."

1900-1914

A brave new style (under the Sea) and a look back to a naughtier age (Nell Gwynne); Scottish waters are now de rigeur, and angling humour breaks into a wider field.

GUILE.
"Please, mum, will you let Jimmy come with us to Sunday-school?"

WHERE IGNORANCE IS BLISS.

Shepherd. "MON, SANDY, HE'S GOT NAE FLEE ON THE END O' THE LINE."
Sandy (sotto voce). "HAUD YER TONGUE. MON! HE DOES NAE KEN, AND HE'S BETTER WITHOOT IT. HE WAS AYE CATCHIN' HISSELF AND ITHER TRASH!"

JUDGE NOT BY APPEARANCES.

AT ONE END OF THE STRING —"YOU MUST BE A FOOLISH BOY TO FISH DOWN A DRAIN-PIPE."

AT THE OTHER END OF THE STRING.

ADVENTURES OF NELL GWYNNE.—No 28.

Charles said he didn't feel very energetic, somehow, so I suggested that he should go fishing; of course I accompanied him. After we had sat there some hours I hinted to him that perhaps there were some better tiddlebrats to catch elsewhere; he appeared to think the fish he wanted to play with was to be caught a little higher up the bank.

P.S.—My heart flutters so when he looks at me that I feel positively helpless, but, thank goodness, he hasn't found that out yet.

ART IN THE HOME.

Small Customer (to general store-dealer). "MOTHER SAYS AS WOULD YOU MIND WRAPPING UP THE KIPPER IN A HILLUSTRATED PAPER, AS HER WALLS ARE GETTING *VERY* BARE."

AGRICULTURE IN THE HIGHLANDS.

Fisherman. "WHAT ON EARTH DO THEY DO WITH THESE LITTLE PATCHES OF CORN THEY GROW UP HERE?"

Gillie. "WEEL, I'M THENKIN' THEY JUST GROW IT FOR SEED THE NEXT YEAR."

DRY-FLY ENTOMOLOGY.

SCENE.—The banks of a Hampshire stream in the Grayling Season

Angler (the rise having abruptly ceased). "I THINK THEY'RE TAKING A *SIESTA*, THOMPSON."

Keeper. "I DESSAY THEY ARE, SIR, BUT ANY OTHER FLY WITH A TOUCH O' RED IN IT WOULD DO AS WELL."

"EXEMPLI GRATIA."

Ancient Mariner (to credulous Yachtsman). "A'MIRAL LORD NELSON! BLESS YER, I KNOWED HIM; SERVED UNDER HIM. MANY'S THE TIME I'VE AS'ED HIM FOR A BIT O' 'BACCO, AS I MIGHT BE A ASTIN' O' YOU; AND SAYS HE, 'WELL, I AIN'T GOT NO 'BACCO,' JEST AS YOU MIGHT SAY TO ME; 'BUT HERE'S A SHILLIN' FOR YER,' SAYS HE"!!

COLD COMFORT.

Nervous Angler (near fort practising at target). "I—I SAY! THIS IS AWFULLY DANGEROUS!"
Old Salt. "OH, IT'S ALL RIGHT, SIR. THERE'D BE AN AWFUL ROW IF THEY SUNK US."

CRITICAL.

Boatman (spelling). "P-S-Y-C-H-E. WELL, THAT'S THE RUMMEST WAY I EVER SEE O' SPELLIN' *FISH!*"

TWO OF THEM!

Rustic. "WELL, MISS, I BE FAIR MAZED WI' THE WAYS O' THAT 'ERE FISHERMAN—THAT I BE!"
Parson's Daughter. "WHY IS THAT, CARVER?"
Rustic. "THE OWD FOOL HAS BEEN SITTIN' THERE FUR THE LAST SIX HOURS AND HASN'T CAUGHT NOTHIN'."
Parson's Daughter. "HOW DO YOU KNOW THAT?"
Rustic. "I'VE BEEN A-WATCHIN' O' HE THE WHOLE TIME!"

Fisherman. "Here comes another dead fish, Pat; the river's full of them. What's the meaning of it?"
Pat. "Sure, I cannot tell at all at all, Sorr, onless it's this terrible fut and mouth disease."

Mid-Channel Mermaids. "Oh! What *funny* tails!"

THE LAST STRAW.

"Sparrers bitin' well this evenin,' guvner?"

IRISH MEASURE.

Boatman (telling a fishing story). "TROTH, SORR, AND HE WAS A PURTY FISH, AND JUST WHEN I WOULD BE AFTHER BRINGIN' HIM TO THE NET, IF THE OWLD ROD DIDN'T GO AND BREAK IN THREE HALVES!"

Sandy, the local fox-destroyer (enquiring about new tenant). "WHAT'S HE WHEN HE'S AT HAME?"
Gillie. "THEY TELL ME HE DOES NAETHING BUT HUNT FOXES; KEEPS SAXTY DOGS AND TWENTY HORSES FOR 'T."
Sandy. "LOSH ME! IT MAUN BE A FINE TRADE DOON THERE."

"Oh! what do I do now?" "Land it, of course, silly!" "But—haven't I got to play it or something?"

FAR FROM THE MADDING CROWD.

Fisherman. I DON'T SUPPOSE YOU SEE THE PAPERS MUCH UP HERE, BUT YOU'VE PROBABLY HEARD ABOUT THE KING WINNING THE DERBY?"
Boatman. "OO AY, I HEERD TELL O' THAT. HE MAUN BE A GUID RIDER, HIM!"

NOT THE FIRST DISAGREEMENT.

Wife. "ISN'T IT JOLLY TO THINK WE HAVE THE WHOLE DAY BEFORE US? THE BOATMAN SAYS WE COULDN'T GO HOME, EVEN IF WE WANTED TO TILL THE TIDE TURNS, AND THAT'S NOT FOR HOURS AND HOURS YET I'VE GOT ALL SORTS OF LOVELY THINGS FOR LUNCH TOO!"

MORE ORNAMENTAL THAN USEFUL.

"JUST GIVE THAT BIT O' LEAD A BITE ATWEEN YER TEETH, WILL YER, MATIE?"
"AIN'T YE GOT NO TEETH OF YER OWN?"
"I GOT SOME, BUT THERE AIN'T NONE OF 'EM OPPOSITE ONE ANOTHER."

A DOUBTFUL COMPLIMENT.

Fisherman (beginner). "DON'T YOU THINK, PETER, I'VE IMPROVED A GOOD DEAL SINCE I BEGAN?"
Peter (anxious to pay a compliment). "YOU HAVE, SORR. BUT SURE IT WAS AISY FOR *YOU* TO IMPROVE, SORR!"

UNDER THE SEA.

Hawker. "YER DON'T WANT TO BUY A NICE LITTLE OCTOPUS, DO YER, GUV'NOR?"

Exhilarated Visitor (leaving Club). "THE FELLER WHO CAUGHT THAT FISH'S DEM LIAR."

THE UNDEFEATABLE ANGLER (ONE OF THE BULLDOG BREED).

A DAY WITH THE FLY.

Customer. "Are they fresh?"
Fishmonger. "Fresh, lady! Why, they was swimmin' in the sea this mornin'! Fresh! Lor' bless—— Lie down, ye devils!"

Sexton (to young farmer who has called to arrange for the christening of his child). "Doantee bring 'e Toosday—Vicar be fishing o' Toosday."
Farmer. "Well, then, say Monday." *Sexton.* "Noa—not Monday. Font'll be full o' minnows Monday."

A PROBLEM FOR ANGLERS.

WILL MR. B. RESCUE MRS. B. BEFORE OR AFTER HE LANDS HIS FIRST SALMON?

UNFEELING.

Ethel (to suffering kinsman). "YOU SHALL HAVE THIS TO-NIGHT, UNCLE—FRIED IN BUTTER!"

THE SEARCH FOR OLYMPIC TALENT.

An ex-swimming champion, accompanied by a friend for timing, disguises himself as a shark at a popular seaside resort.

THE OPPORTUNIST IN THE THAMES VALLEY.

Mr. Crabbe augments his stock-in-trade.

Whisky Galore

Where there's nae whusky there's nae fush, seems to be the sentiment of most gillies and their close cousins, old salts.

IRRESISTIBLE.

Fisherman (chaffing Pensioner). "THEY TELL ME, KENNY, THAT ALL YOUR OLD-AGE PENSION GOES IN DRINK."

Kenny. "NO, MAN, NO' A PENNY O' MY PENSION AM I SPENDIN' ON THE DRINK."

Fisherman. "WHERE DO YOU GET THE MONEY FOR WHISKY, THEN?"

Kenny. "JUST FROM REAL GENTLEMEN LIKE YERSEL."

A WARNING TO LAWSONITES.

First Scotch Boatman. "WEEL, GEORDIE, HOO GOT YE ON THE DAY?"

Second Ditto (drouthy, he had been out with a Free Kirk Minister, a strict abstainer). "NAE AVA. THE AULD CARLE HAD NAE WHUSKEY, SAE I TOOK HIM WHAUR THERE WAS NAE FUSH!"

QUANTITY, NOT QUALITY.

English Angler, having discovered there are two sorts of Whisky at the Inn (best at 6d., second best at 3d.), orders a glass each of the Sixpenny.

Gillie (in a whisper to the Maid as she passes). "MAKE MINE TWA O' THE THREEPENNY!"

A SIN OF OMISSION.

Modest but unsuccessful tyro (who has been flogging the river for hours). "IS THERE ANYTHING I AM OMITTING TO DO, MCWHIRE?"
McW. "I WADNA JUST SAY THAT EXACTLY. BUT I'M THINKIN' YE DRINK VARRA LEETLE WHUSKY FOR A MAN WHAE'S NO KILLIN' FUSH."

1914-1939

Peaceful pursuits among the shells, an odd Norwegian story, H. E. Bateman's work is seen (The Great Strike), and a painter-angler's all-too familiar comment on the river.

THE COMPLEAT OUTPOST.

FLAMBOYANT TOURIST (*hoping to impress fair angler*): "THAT SALMON I GOT YESTERDAY SCALED 18 LBS. 12 OZS."
HEARTLESS FRIEND: "COUNTING THE TINS, I SUPPOSE?"

SOME CATCH: THE ANGLER'S DREAM.

THERE WAS A STREAM IN NORROWAY.

I.—CONVERSATION.

"*Min lille datter*," observes the phrase-book in its maudlin way—"*min lille datter loeser pent*"—My little daughter reads nicely. Well, I daresay she does. But that isn't Norwegian. Norway is not interested in the triumphs of little daughters. Norway is rocky, hard. Norway consists of rapid water and chunks of stone. Especially of rapid water.

"*Ingen fiske*"—no fish; "*anden flue*"—another fly; "*han skal ikke*"—he will not. That is Norwegian. How little these phrase-books know!

The stream is still there, I suppose. The water still flows down creamy and deafening over the shallows, oily and green over the great dark pools. The banks—but Norwegian rivers do not really have banks. On each side of them lie a number of monoliths which have broken off the mountains. These are interspersed with precipices, pinnacles, scaurs, crags, ravines and caves.

Some of the boulders in the bed of a Norwegian stream are about the size of the National Gallery, and some are actually a little smaller; but they are all slippery. They that go down to the bed of a Norwegian stream to fish in it reel to and fro, and stagger like a drunken man; and their conversation is topical and brief.

"Give me the two-handed engine," I might have cried poetically to the gillie, "and let me stand ready to smite once and smite no more." But I never did cry that. I hadn't the time and I didn't know the Norwegian for it. I climbed upon my appointed rock, and he handed me the rod, and I said "*Tak.*" When I had finished my little balancing act I let him have it again, and he said "*Tak*" to me. For "*Tak*" in Norway means the opposite of what it means in Scotland. It means "Thank you."

It was the great word, in fact, this *Tak*, between the gillie and me. When we had exhausted all that idle chatter which I mentioned about fishes and flies, we used to fall back upon *Tak*, and I at least attempted to throw into that beautiful word every subtle variation of which it is capable—pathos, determination, recklessness, despair—as I lurched from boulder to boulder. To him, of course, the boulders were like a ball-room floor. He ran them as the salmon run streams—some streams.

Well, he is still there, I suppose, along with the birch-trees and precipices and the yellow Norwegian ponies with arched necks and little bells and zebra-like markings on their forelegs, who grazed beside the stream wherever there was a place to graze. And the hotel is still there; and Anna, who never ceased to serve meals all day long and smile. And a pair of shoes that I left behind. Oh, yes, and the mosquitoes. There is some of the old Viking blood in the Norwegian mosquitoes. Some of the old Viking blood and some of mine. You can see the traces still, but they are disappearing rapidly. There is no word for mosquitoes in my Norwegian phrase-book, so I always used an English one. More than one, to be precise.

FANCY FISHING IN NORWAY.

I started reading the phrase-book, I remember, in the train to Newcastle. I was full of high hopes then, though anxious. I was anxious about my luggage and clothes. I hadn't a salmon-rod in a long dark coffin, as most of these people had, because I was to use one of Richardson's rods. Richardson was my host. Richardson is the kind of man who has two or more of everything to spare. I shall speak later about Richardson's fishing gear. I had a trout-rod with me, and tried my best to conceal it in the rack. People might have supposed that I was going to fish for salmon with it. It had the appearance in that company of a child's toy. A very stout man was sitting opposite me, with large bulbous eyes. I felt certain all through the journey that he had spotted my trout-rod. I knew him instinctively for a past master in the awful machinery of salmon-fishing.

"What is this fellow doing," I could almost hear him think, "carrying a trout-rod to Newcastle?"

I wished that I had brought at least one salmon-fly to wear in my hat. I opened my phrase-book warily, trying to hold it as if it were a novel by Mr. P. G. WODEHOUSE, and smiling every now and then, though I was really working hard at the pronunciation. Suggestion for the publishers of phrase-books: Have a spare wrapper folded up inside them with the coloured picture of a beautiful girl upon it.

Just before we reached Newcastle the very stout man leaned across and tapped me on the knee.

"Are you going to Norway?" he asked.

"I am," I murmured, stricken with terror and glancing up at the rack.

"Ah!" he said, "it's a very fine country, Norway. I'm in the timber trade myself."

I remember that first reading of my phrase-book for another reason now that I have come home from Norway. It is because I never opened it there. Looking at it again, I can only wonder why. Perhaps the chief reason was that I seldom had it conveniently near me during the crises which called most loudly for its use—when, for instance, I shipped four or five gallons of water in my waders; when I was replacing the clothes on the Norwegian idea of a bed, or when I was trying to stop the steam pressure in the *Dampskib* bath. The Norwegians call a steamer a *Dampskib* in their rough jesting way, and the baths in the Bergen boats, which are pumped out of the grey North Sea, are heated (I suppose from the boiler) by means of rubber tubes. If you cannot find the tap which turns the *Damp* off you either have to shout for the stewardess in the middle of your bath or else die of *Damp*. If I had had

THE GREAT STRIKE.

Mike (discussing a particular fly). "IT WAS THAT LOIKE THE RALE THING, YER HONOUR, THAT IF YE WAS TO LAVE IT DOWN A MINNIT IT'S THE SPIDERS WOULD BE AITIN' UT ON YE."

Local Mariner. "There's a man-eating shark out in the bay."
Visitor. "Extraordinary how some people will eat anything!"

First Tommy. "Ullo, mate, any luck?"
Second Ditto. "No, 'tain't no bloomin' good with them blighters disturbin' the water like this."

HOW PAINTABLE THE RIVER LOOKS WHEN I GO FISHING—

AND HOW FISHABLE IT LOOKS WHEN I GO PAINTING!

'Please Sir!'

Apt words from infants in the days when we were all very young. Do *you* know when the tide is expected back?

"PLEASE, SIR, WHEN'S THE TIDE EXPECTED BACK?"

Dry-fly Expert. "NOW BEFORE I CAN CATCH ANY OF THE FISH HERE I'VE GOT TO IMITATE THE FLY THAT'S ON THE WATER."
Boy. "OH, PLEASE, SIR, MAY I SEE YOU LOOKING LIKE A FLY ON THE WATER?"

FIXING THE BLAME.

"WELL, TOMMY, CAUGHT ANYTHING?"

"NO, I DON'T BELIEVE THE SILLY WORM WAS TRYING."

Small but ardent Butterfly-hunter. "PLEASE, DID YOU EVER CATCH A PURPLE EMPEROR?"

1939-1977

If the general's wife isn't biting perhaps she's in the bathing scene . . . the strip brings us up to date with the short, angular silent humour of our own time.

Drawn by Leo Cheney.

TRAMP : " Guvnor, I'm getting desperate—I ain't 'ad a bite all day—and if I don't get—"
UNLUCKY ANGLER : " Damme, and how many do you think I've had, eh ? "

Drawn by Wilson Fenning.

INDIGNANT FISHERMAN : " That's it ! Just like the lot o' you bloomin' motorists—all you thinks of is your own pleasure—comin' bangin' in 'ere spoilin' a poor bloke's fishin' ! "

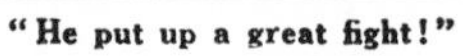
"He put up a great fight!"

THE SPORTING SPIRIT
or, The Other Side of the Wall.

"WHAT? AH MUSTNA FUSH FROM THE PIER? AM AH TO STARVE, THEN, WHILE AH'M DOON HERE?"

"THEY'VE PROPERLY SPOILT OUR FISHING, SAM. BUT, AFTER ALL, IT AIN'T SO BAD, AND THE SEA AIR IS DOING US GOOD."

VERDI
VERDI

Voice from the Bridge. "HULLO, GENERAL! HOW'S YOUR WIFE?"
Angler (rather deaf). "BAD, MY BOY—VERY BAD. WON'T BITE AT ALL TO-DAY."

S-22

CORK

209

CORK

S-165
NO FISHING

NO FISHING

NO FISHING
CORK